Animal Architects

Description

Students explore the phenomenon of squirrels changing their environment to meet their needs by burying seeds. They add to their understanding by reading a nonfiction book and watching videos to learn how other animals, such as gopher tortoises and beavers, engineer structures that affect their environment. They are then challenged to create a paper collage to illustrate the idea that animals can change their environment to meet their needs.

Alignment With the *Next Generation Science Standards*

Performance Expectation		
K-ESS2-2: Construct an argument supported by evidence for how plants and animals (including humans) can change the environment to meet their needs.		
Science and Engineering Practices	**Disciplinary Core Ideas**	**Crosscutting Concepts**
Asking Questions and Defining Problems Ask questions based on observations to find more information about the natural and/or designed world(s). **Engaging in Argument From Evidence** Construct an argument with evidence to support a claim. **Obtaining, Evaluating, and Communicating Information** Obtain information using various texts, text features (e.g., headings, tables of contents, glossaries, electronic menus, icons), and other media that will be useful in answering a scientific question and/or supporting a scientific claim.	**ESS2.E: Biogeology** Plants and animals can change their environment.	**Systems and System Models** Systems in the natural and designed world have parts that work together.

Note: The activities in this lesson will help students move toward the performance expectation listed, which is the goal after multiple activities. However, the activities will not by themselves be sufficient to reach the performance expectation.

Featured Picture Books

TITLE: ***Squirrels Leap, Squirrels Sleep***
AUTHOR: **April Pulley Sayre**
ILLUSTRATOR: **Steve Jenkins**
PUBLISHER: **Henry Holt and Company**
YEAR: **2016**
GENRE: **Poetry**
SUMMARY: *Lyrical text, paired with collage art, offers a glimpse into the fascinating world of squirrels.*

TITLE: ***We Build Our Homes***
AUTHOR: **Laura Knowles**
ILLUSTRATOR: **Chris Madden**
PUBLISHER: **Quarto Publishing**
YEAR: **2018**
GENRE: **Non-Narrative Information**
SUMMARY: *From towering termite mounds to intricate beaver dams, an incredible variety of burrows, nests, and other structures found in nature is showcased here.*

Time Needed

This lesson will take several class periods. Suggested scheduling is as follows:

Session 1: **Engage** with *Squirrels Leap, Squirrels Sleep* Introduction, **Explore** with Squirrel Video, and **Explain** with *Squirrels Leap, Squirrels Sleep* Read-Aloud

Session 2: **Explore** with Looking for Signs and **Explain** with Our Observations

Session 3: **Elaborate** with Animal Architects Card Sort, *We Build Our Homes* Read-Aloud, and Animal Architects Videos

Session 4: **Evaluate** with Collage Art and Writing Activity

Materials

For Animal Architects Card Sort (per student)

• Scissors and glue stick

For Paper Collage (per class)

• A variety of collage-making materials such as construction paper, scrapbook paper, tissue paper, newsprint, magazine pages, and faux fur

National Science Teaching Association

- Real or artificial leaves, twigs, acorns, or dried grass (check for allergies)
- Googly eyes of different sizes
- Scissors
- Glue sticks and white glue
- Watercolor paints
- Paintbrushes
- 9 × 12 (or larger) paper for matting completed collages

Student Pages

- Animal Architects Card Sort and one half sheet of Animals Cards to cut out
- One of the following Animal Templates per student (Squirrel, Woodpecker, Gopher Tortoise, Beaver)
- How Animals Change Their Environment
- STEM Everywhere

In advance, locate an appropriate place on the school grounds to look for signs of animals or plants changing their environment (squirrel nests, bird nests, holes in trees, anthills, grass growing through blacktop, tree roots breaking concrete, etc.) If your schoolgrounds are not conducive to observing nature, schedule a field trip to a park, nature center, or wildlife area. Check your district policy on taking students outside during the school day or away from the school grounds before doing the outdoor activity.

Background for Teachers

Learning about *biogeology*, or the interactions between the organisms on our planet and the planet itself, begins with an understanding of how plants and animals depend on the land, water, and air to live and grow, and how they in turn can change the physical characteristics of their *environment*. Children can easily observe one very common North American mammal changing its environment: the squirrel. In this lesson, students observe videos of squirrels and ask questions about their behaviors, which addresses the science and engineering practice (SEP) of asking questions and defining problems.

Squirrels depend on trees for survival. They collect and roll leaves to make nests high up in branches. Sometimes they nest in abandoned tree holes excavated by woodpeckers. They gather seeds such as acorns, and store them just beneath the surface of the soil for eating during cold months. They use their sharp claws to dig the holes in which to bury the seeds. The acorns that the squirrels don't dig up can grow into oak trees. This *caching* behavior is very important for the renewal of many tree species, especially trees producing heavy seeds that have few chances to sprout when they fall near the parent plant. These relationships illustrate the crosscutting concept (CCC) of systems and system models. The squirrels depend on the trees, and the trees depend on the squirrels. Both parts are necessary for the system to function.

There are many other examples of interactions between organisms and their environments that young children can observe. They can look for evidence of "animal architects" such as bird nests and observe

the different earth materials used to create these structures, including sticks, grass, mud, and stones. They can find evidence of woodpeckers *excavating* nest cavities in trees. They can learn how animals that dig burrows, such as gopher tortoises, change Earth's surface. To make a burrow, these dry-land reptiles found in the southern United States scrape away the top layer of soil with their shovel-like front legs. As they dig, they push soil up to the surface. The soil is now loosened and exposed to the elements. Wind and water can carry it away. This movement of soil from one place to another is called *erosion*. Some animals can change Earth's surface by *deposition*. Deposition occurs when wind or water lays down sediment. When beavers build a dam to block the flow of a stream or river, a pond is formed. Water flowing into the pond from the stream or river deposits sediment. Because gopher tortoises and beavers are not as ubiquitous as squirrels, students can watch videos to observe these incredible animal architects.

Students can also observe how plants can change Earth's surface. Tree roots can grow to uplift soil and concrete. They can even break rocks over time. As trees grow in a rocky area, their roots grow into the small cracks in the rock. Slowly, as the tree grows, its roots break the rock apart. This forms more soil and makes it easier for other plants to grow there as well.

In the upper elementary grades, these ideas are expanded to include other ways that living things affect the physical characteristics of their environment. For example, plants' roots hold soil in place, plants' respiration affects the air, and many types of rocks and minerals are formed from the remains of organisms or are altered by their activities. The CCC of systems and system models is addressed by discussing how living things in an ecosystem are interdependent.

Learning Progressions

Below are the DCI grade band endpoints for grades K–2 and 3–5. These are provided to show how student understanding of the DCIs in this lesson will progress in future grade levels.

DCI	Grades K–2	Grades 3–5
ESS2.E: Biogeology	Plants and animals can change their environment.	Living things affect the physical characteristics of their regions.

Source: Willard, T., ed. 2015. *The NSTA quick-reference guide to the* NGSS: *Elementary school.* Arlington, VA: NSTA Press.

engage

Squirrels Leap, Squirrels Sleep Introduction

Making Connections: Text to Self

Show the cover of the book, read the title, and introduce the author and illustrator. *Ask*

? Have you ever seen a squirrel leap?

? Have you ever seen a squirrel sleep?

? Where do squirrels sleep?

? Where have you seen squirrels?

? What have you seen squirrels doing?

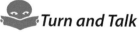**Turn and Talk**

Invite students to share with a partner their knowledge about and experiences with squirrels.

Tell students that the author, April Pulley Sayre, has written over 65 books about nature. She lives in Indiana and has a large yard she calls her "wildlife garden." It is full of trees, bushes, wildflowers, butterflies, hummingbirds, and even a pond. She loves to watch the squirrels that live in her yard. Tell students that before they read the book, they are going to get a chance to watch a squirrel in action!

explore

Squirrel Video

GRAY SQUIRREL BURYING A NUT

Show all or part of the 3:21 minute video "Squirrel Hiding His Nuts HD" from YouTube (see Websites section) or a similar video of a squirrel. Have the students observe the squirrel's behaviors, and then infer why the squirrel is doing those behaviors.

After the students watch the video, *ask*

? What were some of the things we saw the squirrel doing? (digging, eating food, burying food, sitting up and listening for danger, etc.)

? How did the squirrel change its environment? In other words, what was the squirrel doing that changed the earth? (digging up food, burying food)

? How did the squirrel bury the food? (by digging a small hole with its claws, pushing around with its head, putting the food in the hole, and covering it up)

? Why do squirrels bury food? (Answers will vary, but some students may know that squirrels bury food to save it for later or to protect it from other animals.)

> **SEP: Asking Questions and Defining Problems**
> Ask questions based on observations to find more information about the natural world.

After discussing the questions above, *ask*

? What are you wondering about squirrels?

Record student questions on the board or poster paper.

explain

Squirrels Leap, Squirrels Sleep Read-Aloud

Determining Importance

Tell students that you will now read the book *Squirrels Leap, Squirrels Sleep*. Have them listen for any answers to their questions about squirrels. In addition to the main text, read the back matter called "Tree Hole Homes" about how squirrels often nest in tree holes that woodpeckers have made and abandoned. This section also describes the leaf nests made by squirrels high up in tree branches.

After reading, open to the book's second two-page spread that shows four different kinds of squirrels and *ask*

? What were the different kinds of squirrels pictured in the book? (gray squirrel, fox squirrel, red squirrel, and flying squirrel)

? Where do squirrels sleep? (in tree holes made by woodpeckers, or in leaf nests made by the squirrels)

? Have you ever seen a squirrel nest? What do squirrel nests look like? (Some students may have noticed squirrels coming out of a hole in a tree, or may have seen their large leaf nests in trees when the branches are bare.)

? What were the squirrels in the book eating? (acorns)

? What did they do with some of the acorns? (They buried them.)

? Why did they bury them? (to eat later)

? After the winter, what happened to some of the acorns? (They sprouted, grew roots, turned into seedlings, etc.)

? What do you think acorns grow into? (Some students will know that acorns grow into oak trees.)

? The land, water, or air in which animals and plants live in or on is known as their *environment*. How do squirrels change their environment? In other words, what do squirrels do to change the place where they live? (They build nests, they dig in the dirt, and they bury acorns that can grow into trees.)

? What would happen to a forest if squirrels didn't bury acorns and other seeds? (Answers will vary, but students may infer that not as many trees would grow.)

? What are some other ways that animals change their environment? (Answers will vary.)

CCC: Systems and System Models
Systems in the natural world have parts that work together.

Revisit the list of questions that students generated about squirrels. Ask them what questions have been answered by the book. Then ask if they have any more questions to add after reading. Explain that in science, as we learn more, we often have more questions. Continue to add student questions to the chart as you proceed with the lesson.

explore

Looking for Signs

Tell students that they will be exploring outside to look for signs of squirrels and other animals and plants changing their environment. In advance, locate an appropriate place on the school grounds to look for signs of animals or plants changing their environment such as squirrel nests, bird nests, anthills, burrows, grass growing through blacktop, and tree roots breaking concrete. If your schoolgrounds are not conducive to observing nature, schedule a field trip to a park, nature preserve, or wetland area to look for these signs. During the nature hike, have students walk quietly and look for signs of animals or plants changing their environment. You may want to take a camera to record their findings.

LOOKING FOR CHANGES IN THE ENVIRONMENT

explain

Our Observations

After the hike, have students share their observations and wonderings. *Ask*

? Did you see any squirrels?

? Did you find any signs of squirrels changing their environment (the earth, air, and water

they live in or on)? (Students may have seen leaf nests in trees, or noticed squirrels digging in the ground.)

? What would happen if squirrels did not live there? (not as many trees would grow, ground would not be dug up, no nests in trees, etc.)

? Did you see any other animals?

? Did you find any signs of other animals changing their environment?

? Did you find any signs of plants changing their environment? (roots pushing up through concrete, etc.)

CCC: Systems and System Models
Systems in the natural world have parts that work together.

---

elaborate

Animal Architects Card Sort

Connecting to the Common Core
Reading: Informational Text
CRAFT AND STRUCTURE: K.5

Determining Importance

Introduce the author and illustrator of *We Build Our Homes.* Share and identify the front cover, back cover, and title page. *Ask*

? From looking at the cover, what do you think this book is about? (Answers will vary.)

Write the word *architect* on the board. Ask students to listen for what that word means as you read pages 6 and 7, "Born to Build."

Stop after reading pages 6 and 7, and *ask*

? What is an architect? (a person who designs buildings or other structures)

? How can animals be like architects? (They can build things.)

? How are squirrels like architects? (They build nests in trees.)

? What are some of the reasons animals change their environment by building? (to keep babies safe in nests, to hide from predators, to stay warm in winter, to stay cool in summer, to store food, to impress a mate, etc.)

Tell students that in the book *We Build Our Homes,* they will learn how three different animals change their environment by building things. Before reading any more of the book, pass out the Animal Architects Card Sort, and have the students cut out the animal picture cards.

You can do the first one together to model how to match the squirrel (#1) to its leaf nest (D). Students may want to match the squirrel to the tree hole, but remind them that squirrels don't actually build their own tree holes. Then, have students match the rest of the animals to the homes they

MATCHING ANIMALS TO THEIR HOMES

build. Students will have the opportunity to move their cards as you read the book. Note: All of the animals on the Animal Architects Card Sort student page appear in *We Build Our Homes* except the squirrel.

We Build Our Homes Read-Aloud

Features of Nonfiction

Explain that, because this book is nonfiction, you can start reading on any page. You don't have to read the book from cover to cover if you are looking for specific information. Tell students that parts of this book will help them match their animal cards with the home each animal builds. After you read each two-page spread, have students move their cards if necessary.

### Chunking

Follow the steps below to "chunk" the book into three main sections. Note that you will not read the entire book aloud for this activity. (You may choose to read more of the book later, but it is only necessary to read these four two-page spreads for the card sort activity.)

1. Great Spotted Woodpeckers: Read pages 20–21, about these woodpeckers and the neat round holes in trees they make to raise their chicks.

2. Gopher Tortoises: Read pages 40–41, about how these hard-shelled *excavators* dig underground tunnels to stay safe from predators and forest fires. Many other animals also use the gopher tortoise tunnels.

3. Beavers: Read pages 54–55, about how beavers fell trees to build a dam that turns a stream into a pond. Then they build a cozy lodge in the pond to live in and raise their young.

4. End by reading pages 58–59, about how humans build tunnels, towers, ships, villages, and cities. Then discuss the last two sentences: "We may be clever builders, but we are not alone. We must all share this

world, this one planet we call home."

After reading, students may glue the cards onto the Animal Architects student page once they are all in the correct places. The answers to the Animal Architects Card Sort are as follows:

1. Squirrel – D. Leaf Nest
2. Woodpecker – C. Tree Hole
3. Gopher Tortoise – B. Burrow
4. Beaver – A. Lodge

> **SEP: Obtaining, Evaluating, and Communicating Information**
> Obtain information using various texts, text features, and other media that will be useful in answering a scientific question and/or supporting a scientific claim.

Animal Architects Videos

Tell students that you have some interesting videos of animal architects in action. The first shows a pileated woodpecker, a relative of the great spotted woodpecker from the book *We Build Our Homes*. Pileated woodpeckers live in many parts of North America and *excavate*, or chisel out, nests in trees to raise their young. Partway through the video the motion is sped-up and accompanied by the William Tell Overture (commonly known as the *Lone Ranger* theme song).

> **CCC: Systems and System Models**
> Systems in the natural world have parts that work together.

Show the 1:35-minute video "Timelapse of a Pileated Woodpecker Creating a Cavity" (see "Websites") and then *ask*

? How does the woodpecker change its environment? (by chiseling holes into trees)

? Why does it change its environment? (to make a nest for its chicks)

? How do you think the tree holes might help other animals? (Students may know that other animals, such as squirrels and wood ducks, sometimes use abandoned woodpecker nests to raise their young.)

? What would happen to the other animals if the woodpecker did not make the hole in the tree? (They might not be able to find a safe nesting place for their babies.)

Show the 3:47-minute video "Gopher Tortoises Burrowing to Escape Forest Fires" (see "Websites") and then *ask*

? How does the gopher tortoise change its environment? (by digging tunnels or burrows in the ground)

? Why does it change its environment? (to escape predators and forest fires)

? How does the burrow help other animals? (The other animals can escape predators and forest fires too.)

? What would happen to the other animals if the tortoise did not dig the burrow? (They might not be able to escape the predators or fires.)

Next, show the 2:48-minute video, "Hardworking Builders" (see "Websites") about how beavers build dams and then *ask*

? How do the beavers change their environment—the earth, water, or air they live in or on? (by cutting down trees to build a dam)

? Why do they change their environment? (to turn a stream into a pond)

? How do you think other animals might be helped by beavers building a dam? (They can live in and around the pond.)

? What would happen to the other animals if the beavers did not build the dam? (They would not have a pond to live in or around.)

evaluate

Collage Art and Writing Activity

Connecting to the Common Core
Reading: Informational Text
CRAFT AND STRUCTURE: K.6

Show the cover of *Squirrels Leap, Squirrels Sleep* and ask students for their ideas on how Steve Jenkins made the pictures for the book. Then explain that Steve Jenkins uses an art form called *paper collage*. With this technique, bits and pieces of different colors, shapes, and types of paper are combined to create the artwork.

Determining Importance

Ask students to observe the steps that the artist takes to make the collage in the 4:19-minute video called "Create a Collage With Steve Jenkins" (see "Websites"). Have students describe the steps he used to create the frog in the video (make a thumbnail sketch, draw an outline of a frog on the back of colored paper, cut out the outline of the body, glue the body on another piece of paper, cut out the legs, etc.). Explain that there are many illustrators, such as Steve Jenkins and Eric Carle, who use various collage techniques to illustrate picture books.

Then tell students that they are going to get the chance to use a paper-collage technique to make a two-dimensional (flat) model of an animal changing its environment. First, brainstorm ways that squirrels and other animals change their environment (the earth, water, and air they live in or on). Students should think about the two books that were read, what they observed on the Looking for Signs nature hike, the videos they watched, and what they have observed in their own lives. Some examples include the following:

- Squirrels bury nuts in the ground.
- Squirrels build nests in trees.
- Woodpeckers make holes in trees.

- Birds build nests.
- Ants build anthills.
- Gopher tortoises dig burrows in the ground.
- Beavers cut down trees.
- Beavers build dams and lodges in the water.

Writing

Then show students the four templates they can choose from to make their model: squirrel, woodpecker, gopher tortoise, and beaver. (Feel free to let them draw an animal other than those pictured on the templates.) You may want to show some examples of animal collage art (see "Gerren Lamson Woodland Creatures" in the "Websites" section). Then, go over the instructions below:

1. Paint the background: Does your animal change its environment in the trees, water, or earth? What colors could you use to represent trees, water, or earth? Use watercolor paints to paint the colors of trees, water, or earth on the entire paper. Don't worry that you are painting over the animal outline—you will fill in that part in the next step. Let the paint dry. Begin cutting, tearing, or wadding paper for the next step.

2. Create the collage. Fill in the outline of your animal by gluing on torn, cut, or wadded construction paper, newsprint, tissue paper, or other materials. Then add details such as googly eyes and real or artificial leaves, twigs, acorns, or dried grass. Be creative!

3. Write about the model: On the How Animals Change Their Environment student page, explain how your animal changes its environment by completing the sentence. For example, "<u>Squirrels</u> change their environment by <u>burying nuts in the ground</u>."

PAPER COLLAGE

4. Mat the finished collage by gluing it to a larger piece of paper. Attach the completed student page to the bottom of the collage and display.

> **SEP: Engaging in Argument From Evidence**
> Construct an argument with evidence to support a claim.

This writing piece can be used to evaluate whether students understand that animals can change their environment to meet their needs. Encourage students to be creative and to use their imaginations when choosing materials and making their models. You may want to display the completed collages with the heading "Animal Architects."

STEM Everywhere

Give students the STEM Everywhere student page as a way to involve their families and extend their learning. They can do the activity with an adult helper and share their results with the class. If students do not have access to the internet at home, you may choose to have them complete this activity at school.

Opportunities for Differentiated Instruction

This box lists questions and challenges related to the lesson that students may select to research, investigate, or innovate. Students may also use the questions as examples to help them generate their own questions. These questions can help you move your students from the teacher-directed investigation to engaging in the science and engineering practices in a more student-directed format.

Extra Support

For students who are struggling to meet the lesson objectives, provide a question and guide them in the process of collecting research or helping them design procedures or solutions.

Extensions

For students with high interest or who have already met the lesson objectives, have them choose a question (or pose their own question), conduct their own research, and design their own procedures or solutions.

After selecting one of the questions in this box or formulating their own questions, students can individually or collaboratively make predictions, design investigations or surveys to test their predictions, collect evidence, devise explanations, design solutions, or examine related resources. They can communicate their findings through a science notebook, at a poster session or gallery walk, or by producing a media project.

Research

Have students brainstorm researchable questions:

? How do squirrels find the nuts they have hidden?

? What kinds of materials do birds use to build nests?

? Why don't woodpeckers get concussions?

Investigate

Have students brainstorm testable questions to be solved through science or math:

? Set up a squirrel feeder outside the classroom window. Then count the squirrels twice a day. Do more squirrels come to the feeder in the morning or afternoon? Graph the results, and then analyze your graph. What can you conclude?

? Set up two or more different squirrel feeders outside the classroom window, with a different food in each (peanuts, sunflower seeds, corn, etc.) Which feeder do the squirrels go to more often? Graph the results, and then analyze your graph. What can you conclude?

Continued

Opportunities for Differentiated Instruction (*continued*)

Innovate

Have students brainstorm problems to be solved through engineering:

? Can you design a squirrel feeder?

? Can you design a squirrel-proof bird feeder?

? Can you design a model of a bird nest or beaver dam?

Websites

 "Create a Collage With Steve Jenkins" Video
www.youtube.com/watch?v=jdk2173Ej3U

 "Gerren Lamson Woodland Creatures"
http://www.gerrenlamson.com/play/woodland-creatures.htm

 "Gopher Tortoises: Burrowing to Escape Forest Fires" Video
https://cet.pbslearningmedia.org/resource/nat15.sci.lisci.gopher/gopher-tortoises-burrowing-to-escape-forest-fires

 "Hardworking Builders" (Beavers) Video
https://cet.pbslearningmedia.org/resource/nat14.sci.lifsci.builders/hardworking-builders

 "Squirrel Hiding His Nuts HD" Video
www.youtube.com/watch?v=qUyLzRAFWPg

 "Timelapse of a Pileated Woodpecker Creating a Cavity" Video
https://vimeo.com/125308260

 Woodpecker video is also available on YouTube at *www.youtube.com/watch?v=LPiCAPibtr4*

More Books to Read

Aston, D. H. 2015. *A nest is noisy*. New York: Chronicle Books.
Summary: From tiny hummingbird nests wrapped in spider's silk to papery hornet nests made from chewed wood, an incredible variety of nests is showcased here in brilliant splendor.

Evans, S. 2018. *Animal homes*. New York: National Geographic Kids.
Summary: This book for pre-readers features activities to build comprehension, such as a vocabulary tree and a wrap-up activity, to help them make connections between words and expand their understanding of how and why animals build homes.

Jenkins, S., and R. Page. 2016. *I see a kookaburra*. New York: HMH Books for Young Readers.
Summary: Jenkins's trademark paper-collage artwork depicts six different habitats and the animals that live in each.

Raum, E. 2010. Animal Builders Series: *Bears make dens. Beavers build lodges. Orangutans build tree nests. Rabbits dig burrows. Bees build beehives.* Mankato, MN: Amicus Ink.
Summary: Each book in this nonfiction series features a different animal and describes how it makes its home. Includes activities, a glossary, more books to read, and websites.

Animal Cards

Directions: Cut out the pictures of the animals below. Then match each animal to the home it builds.

1. Squirrel	3. Gopher Tortoise
2. Woodpecker	4. Beaver

Animal Cards

Directions: Cut out the pictures of the animals below. Then match each animal to the home it builds.

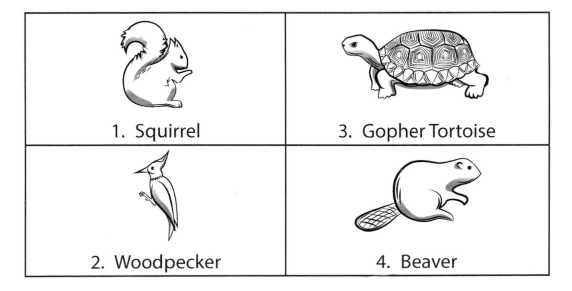

1. Squirrel	3. Gopher Tortoise
2. Woodpecker	4. Beaver

Animal Architects
Card Sort

	A. Lodge
	B. Burrow
	C. Tree Hole
	D. Leaf Nest

National Science Teaching Association

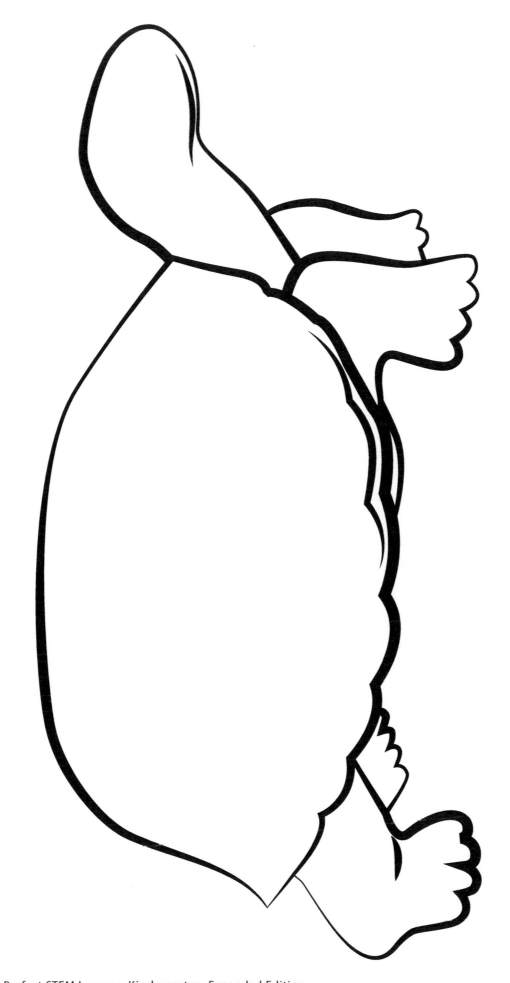

Name: _____

How Animals Change
Their Environment

change their environment by

_____

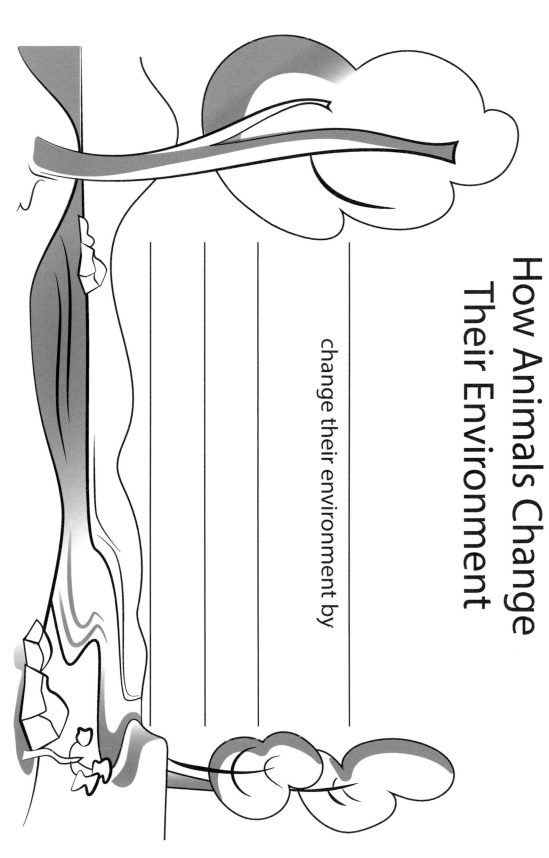

Name: _____

STEM Everywhere

Dear Families,

At school, we have been learning about **how animals change their environment.** Some animals change the earth. Some animals change the trees. Some animals change the water. Many animals are like architects and build homes and other structures. To find out more, ask your learner the following questions and discuss their answers:

- What did you learn?
- What was your favorite part of the lesson?
- What are you still wondering?

At home, you can watch a short video from PBS Learning Media about animal homes. As you watch, discuss the different ways animals build homes. Then you can take a walk in a natural area outside to look for signs of animals building homes or changing their environment in other ways.

 To access the video, scan the QR code, type "Nature Nuggets Animal Homes" into your search engine, or go to *https://cet.pbslearningmedia.org/resource/nuggets.el.sci.homes/nature-nuggets-animal-homes.*

Draw a picture of an animal changing its environment.

┌───┐
│   │
│   │
│   │
│   │
│   │
│   │
│   │
└───┘

National Science Teaching Association